Echoes of Time

... Memories of learning and teaching life's lessons

Worley Faver

SeaDog Press
Ponte Vedra, Florida 32081

Cover Painting: C. Ford Riley

Cover design: SeaDog Press

Editor: Florence Love Karsner

ISBN: 978-1-943369-18-8

Preface

Whilst plundering through some old papers I saved from my childhood and school days, I came upon a short story that was a project required by one of my teachers. This story was written when I was about sixteen or seventeen years old, and I venture to say this piece was my first excursion into the writing world.

When I re-read it recently, it brought back memories as meaningful as those you will read in my latest collection of stories. Most of all, I was pleasantly surprised to see that the young man who wrote this piece still lives in the soul of the old man who spent a lifetime filled with adventures that are expressed in *Echoes of Time*.

Worley Faver
1954

All you hear is the steady thump of the horses hooves
in the damp soft earth. There is a slight mist looming just
above the ground, but still you can see the huge figures of
the ancient oak trees outlined against the rapidly fading
sky. You glance over your shoulder and see the only star
that is still shining and remember that it's not a star but
the planet Venus, which is the last to stop shining in the
early fall. And as you turned you noticed that in the east
there is a lightness which means that dawn is very near. As
you face the trail again and give your horse a shove in the
sides with your knees, to go faster, you think back to the
time this plan first formed in your mind. It was a week ago
that you walked down this very trail and saw the tracks of a
large buck by the edge of a small glade, and then as you looked
closer you noticed that the tracks were very fresh and that
there were many old tracks made by the same deer, using this
trail into the grassy glade. You knew then that the old buck
probably fed in the glade in the early morning then returned
to some patch of woods that were thick enough to sheild him
from the eyes of the many squirrel hunters that roamed the woods
during the day. So, this morning you plan to arrive in time
to catch the deer still feeding. You've come within 50 yards
of the glade now, so you tie your horse to a small pine tree,
and start out on foot. As you walk along, you slip 2 buck
shot into your double barrel shot gun. You find that you are
walking into the wind and know that the deer won't be able to
catch your scent very easily.

Worley Faver

Suddenly, you are startled by the cracking of a small twig,
and look up to see the most unforgetable sight of your life,
there, standing in the trail not 30 feet from where you are,
is the deer that you have been stalking. In the one moment
that he stands staring at you, you see the 6 point antlers
set on top of the majestic head. In the dark brown eyes there
seems to be a flicker of curiosity, but as you make a slight
move, he turns and gracefully runs back across the glade and
into the thick pine woods. For a moment you stand and look
at the dew-laden grass where just x seconds ago stood the
old buck.

Introduction

Echoes of Time is a book, of course, but it's really a collection of short stories—stories which should be enjoyed like a fine sandwich. The backdrop is hunting and fishing, but it is much more than that. Through Worley's keen powers of observation and recollection, life lessons are taught and learned through the enjoyment of the outdoors in the mid-20th century rural North Florida. It's a story not just of good friends, polite living and fireflies, but of guns and men and the explosion of a bass breaking the surface of the water, glittering in the early morning sun.

Echoes of Time is a glimpse back to a simpler, gentler life—one that now seems so far away. Springing from an environment without all of the comforts of modern life, Worley nonetheless had access to everything wonderful that rural America could offer, abundant game, fish and fowl, wild, unpopulated woods, fields and streams, empty beaches and the great Atlantic Ocean.

The book hearkens back to the days when nobody gave a second thought to a nine-year-old boy walking down the street with a cane fishing pole over his shoulder and a handmade slingshot sticking out of his back pocket. Worley paints a picture that takes the reader back to grandpa's day, and the delights of growing up before technology overwhelmed us.

In *Echoes of Time,* Worley captures and conveys the experiences of a fantastic boyhood, and for the overwhelming majority of Americans in today's times, such adventures are found only in stories told by folks from the distant past.

Kyle Summerall

Ponte Vedra Beach, Florida

Dedication

This book is dedicated to Flavian Jacob Mickler – my mentor, teacher, best friend, and brother I never had. One day—fifty years ago—we were in the Guana Management Area at dawn, riding our horses into the rising sun when a flock of roseate spoonbills chose that very moment to take to the sky—directly over our heads—with the sunlight illuminating those rose-colored wings. Flavian said, "Worley, we will never see a more beautiful sight than this." We never did and one day he was gone to the other side.

▧ *Flavian and Fancy*

Acknowledgments

What a wonderful experience it is to have the opportunity to work with the best publisher and editor in the world of stories and books. My publisher, CAPT Garry Karsner, SC, USNR (Ret), and editor and author, Florence Love Karsner, made the whole writing process a pleasure for this old storyteller. They displayed incredible patience, expertise, and untiring effort in helping me create these stories. It was truly a joy to be exposed to their intelligence and good humor. Without their encouragement and friendship, this project would have been impossible.

Foreword

For some time, my friends have asked me to write about my experiences growing up in the woods of Palm Valley before so much development came. The stories in this collection are dated from 1946 – 1980. We Palm Valley menfolk spent a considerable amount of time fishing in the Tolomato River and hunting in the woods of Palm Valley, including what is now the Guana Management Area.

Our cattle and horses were kept in a live oak hammock off Palm Valley Road. Back then, Mr. Herb Peyton was the owner of the properties which covered thousands of acres. He allowed us access to his properties, and his only charge was to ask us to build a barbed-wire fence around them. We did as he asked, and began a project which took months to accomplish. We even built a cross-fence from the Guana River to the Tolomato River, which cut off thousands of acres. We will always be indebted to Mr. Peyton for his kindness to our group of Palm Valley men. These stories are mainly about fishing, hunting, and some of my experiences drilling for oil in the North and South Atlantic and Gulf of Mexico.

My first collection of stories, *River of Time*, captured the essence of a number of special people that were and still are important in my life. A few of them served as mentors and helped guide me as I walked paths I chose to experience life . . . one that has lasted almost eighty-four years.

This book, *Echoes of Time*, recalls experiences with some of these same people and events which would be impossible to duplicate these days.

As a young man full of energy and adventurous longings, I indulged in fishing and hunting wild boar, deer, and alligators. These days I no longer wish to end the life of nature's magnificent creatures, but I can say that we made use of every animal we killed. In fact, my sons were taught very early that they should never kill any creature without cause, and when they did, they should offer thanks to the Great Spirit. The echoes of these adventures now call to me, and I would like to share them with you, my readers.

Table of Contents

1
Palm Valley Boy

Here's how it all began! Mama and Daddy (Samuel Worley Faver and Mary Birdy DeGrove Faver) were living in Palm Valley in 1937. Their little wood framed house was located on Palm Valley Road between the Palm Valley Baptist Church and the house where Mama was born and raised.

Grandpa and Granny DeGrove were still alive and doing well, living in what has always been known as The Big House, which Grandpa

Samuel and Mary DeGrove Faver

built from cypress and stone. On September eleventh, Mama went into labor and Daddy drove her to what is now Jacksonville Beach to see her physician, Dr. Earl Roberts, who was the only doctor at the beach at that time. I was born at 4:00 a.m. on September twelfth in a little house on Third Street, which Dr. Roberts used to deliver babies.

One night in 1940, Granny woke up and discovered Grandpa was not breathing. Apparently, he had died in his sleep. I so wish that I had known him. He was a special man and was a former County Commissioner and State of Florida legislator. He and Granny raised seven children in The Big House. After Grandpa passed to the other side, Mama and Daddy moved into The Big House with Granny.

William and Mary DeGrove

I was three years old. Mama and Daddy sold their little house to Luther and Mary Hughes. Mary's father, Cyrus Turknett, dismantled the house and used the material to expand Mary's house just north on Palm Valley Road.

Those years growing up in The Big House were the perfect childhood for me, and I was probably the most spoiled child in history. By the time I was eleven years old, I was wandering the Palm Valley woods shooting squirrels with my little Winchester .410 shotgun. Sometimes I stayed in the woods too late, and I could hear Mama calling my name from the back door. I would go directly home and clean my squirrels. Then we would have fried squirrel, grits, and collard greens for supper.

On Sundays, Granny, Mama, and I always walked to church for Sunday School and the morning service. Daddy never went to church, but he always stood at the end of The Big House lane and listened to the music, which he loved. When I was twelve years old, I was baptized in the Intracoastal Waterway by Reverend Billy Carmichael.

William Worley Faver, c 1941

Palm Valley was such a special place for a child to grow up. Uncle Charley DeGrove still planted Grandpa's big field across Palm Valley Road, selling the produce to Mr. Crow at Jacksonville Beach, his place being the only grocery store within many miles. Uncle Charley also had spring and summer gardens, one of which was directly behind The Big House. We always had plenty of vegetables, fresh in the summer and canned in the winter. In the fall, sugar cane was grown in the garden. When ripe, the cane was cut and hauled down a dirt road, which is now Canal

Boulevard. The cane mill and syrup kettle were located across the road from Uncle Charlie's house. The kettle was fired with pine fat wood, and the mill boom was pulled around and around by Uncle Charlie's mule. In later years, the boom was turned by an old, cut down Model A Ford, with the steering wheel tied and no one at the wheel. The kids were warned to avoid the Model A, 'cause no one was driving!

The cane stalks were ground in the mill, and the juice poured into the kettle for boiling. I can still see Uncle Charley screening the boiling juice and carefully testing the viscosity of the young syrup. Everyone ended up with enough syrup to last all year. What I wouldn't give for that syrup on my pancakes today!

Here's a story of an interesting afternoon. We young boys loved to play touch football in Aunt Doris and Uncle Cy's front yard, which was just north on Palm Valley Road. Their house and garden sat on at least ten acres.

In those days, most Florida counties allowed dangerous prisoners to maintain the road rights-of-way. Of course, these prisoners would be escorted by a guard or two armed with 12-gauge shotguns. So, there we were having a great old time playing football, only slightly aware of the prisoner work crew slowly coming down Palm Valley Road. All of a sudden, we heard one of the guards shout "halt!" We looked toward the road and saw four prisoners running directly toward us. The guards raised their shotguns but couldn't shoot because we boys were directly in their line of fire. In just a few hours, the prisoners were apprehended and returned to their cells . . . I reckon with longer sentences.

We looked forward all year to the beginning of hunting season, primarily because all the men of our family would camp out one night in the woods. On this night, Uncle Charlie would prepare his world-famous squirrel stew over the camp fire. The young boys were responsible for providing the squirrels. One year Daddy shot a squirrel above the fire, and it almost fell into the cast iron Dutch oven full of stew! The older men would go home to a comfortable bed after eating supper, and the young men would spend the night beneath the trees. I remember one year I killed seventeen squirrels for the stew.

This is just a glimpse of my idyllic childhood and those long-lost precious days.

2

Moonshine

During, and maybe even before Prohibition, moonshine was produced in Palm Valley. Here are a few tales that I remember hearing as a child.

Uncle Joe Townsend, Granny DeGrove's brother, was one of my favorite relatives. One day my sister,

Uncle Joe, c 1940's

Jackie, and Daddy were squirrel hunting not far from The Big House. Daddy said he was walking with Sister looking up into the trees for squirrels, when they walked into a little clearing that Daddy had never seen before. He said, "My Lord, we have walked into Uncle Joe's little still operation and it's cooking!"

No one in the family ever knew where Uncle Joe's still was until then. Daddy said, "This would be a perfect time for the revenuers to raid Uncle Joe's still."

Uncle Joe was one of the more colorful characters from my childhood, and one I will never forget. He was a small, wiry man, a lifelong bachelor and trapper, who lived alone in a little cabin down the road from The Big House. One day I was in his small kitchen and as I looked around, I noticed that all his Maxwell House coffee cans were lined up on a shelf over the stove. When I asked why this was so, Uncle Joe opened one for me. It was full of money. This was his private bank! So, I reckon moonshine and hide sales were pretty good.

Mama and Daddy always drove to the beach on Saturday night to take in a movie. Uncle Joe always showed up to go along, dressed in a black coat and tie with a nice, black fedora on his old head. I also recall that his cheeks were rosy, so I guess he had a drink or three of his product!

The neighbors across the road had a much larger operation than Uncle Joe. They also ran a large herd of woods cattle, because in those days there were no fencing laws.

"Big Red" was the aggressive bull of the herd, and we children were afraid of him. Granny would walk to Aunt Doris' house north on Palm Valley Road and if she came face-to-face with Big Red, she just stared him down and walked past.

When our neighbors were preparing to bring the moonshine in from the still, one of the daughters would climb the tall sycamore tree in the front yard to keep an eye out for the revenuers. When the product was loaded, they would drive to the Diego Plains and turn north onto Possum Trot Road, which in those days ran north and south from Mickler Road to Palm Valley Road. It was a dirt road, and back then A1A traveled along the ocean front. As a precaution, the boys had dug a pit in the road and covered it with brush. Sure enough, one day that pit came in handy. The boys were seen by the revenuers when they turned north on Possum Trot Road and the chase was on. Of course, the driver of the lead vehicle knew to drive around the covered pit, but the chase car went down immediately and was stuck. It is said that on the way home the boys stopped and pulled the revenuers out of the hole. Some of this tale could be true.

In later years, some of our friends across the old canal bridge had a much larger operation. There were stories of chases, but their very fast Ford delivery cars were never caught. The engines in their Fords were set up by a race car mechanic who apparently knew his business.

To my knowledge, only one unlucky moonshiner was ever arrested in Palm Valley. He spent a year and a day in an Atlanta prison. He was a nice, quiet guy and his wife and my mother were good friends. Likewise, their son was one of my friends. Sadly, all three of these good folks have been gone to the other side for a long time.

3

Flavian

From the time I was nine years old, he was my mentor, best friend, and the brother I never had. He was the love of my sister's life and father to three beautiful girls. I grew up literally following his footsteps in the Palm Valley woods.

His name was Flavian Jacob Mickler. He joined the U. S. Navy and went to war after Pearl Harbor, serving in the Pacific. He was an F-4 Corsair mechanic serving on the USS Enterprise (CV-6)— The Galloping Ghost. He told me a few stories of those days, of how the marine gunners would shoot down the kamikaze suicide planes just before they struck the ship, and how the torpedo planes would land, shot up by Japanese gunners, with the remains of a sailor in the back seat. He didn't talk a lot about those experiences.

After the war, he was stationed at Naval Air Station (NAS) Jacksonville. I remember one Saturday when he invited the family to a special airshow, where the newly-founded Blue Angels were to perform. It was a beautiful day with clear blue skies, and the Blue Angels put on a brilliant show. But the show came to an end when one of the Bear Cats made an almost vertical dive in front of the crowd and never pulled out. The plane crashed into the runway and disappeared in a gigantic fireball. Daddy threw me on the ground and covered me with his body. It was a miracle that no one else was injured. God Bless that young Navy pilot.

Flavian and I started hunting together in the late 1940's in what is now the Guana Management Area. Our transportation was an old Model A Ford with a modified body and aircraft tires to handle the muddy roads. Only the military had four-wheel drives in those days. Many years later we hunted on horseback.

Flavian constructed about ten wild hog traps. These traps were six feet by eight feet with hog wire and a sliding door. The sliding door top was attached to a nylon rope, which went over the door frame and had a wooden stake tied to the other end. This stake would fit behind two other stakes driven in the ground. Sour corn would be sprinkled around the ground stakes. The wild hogs could not resist the aroma of the sour corn and would go into the trap through the open door when it was in the raised position. They would start eating the corn and invariably root up the trigger stake and the door would slide down. It was an ingenious design.

Every weekend we would go out and check the traps. We would castrate the boars, crop their tails, and release them. Any sows and young gilts (females) would be released. When we hunted hogs in the fall with the dogs, we would only shoot the ones with cropped tails, which were easy to spot. This practice assured a steady population of hogs and also put prime pork on the table.

4

Gators

Here are a few stories about alligator hunting, beginning with my initiation by Flavian into this world. He was the best woodsman I have ever known.

••••••

When I was about eleven years old, Flavian and I began hunting together in the area that is now owned by the State of Florida and called The Guana Management Area. To local Palm Valley people, it has always been known as "The Neck."

One day in the late 1940's we were looking for gators in The Neck. Flavian was recently discharged from the United States Navy after serving in World War II and was driving his old modified Model A.

We pulled up to an open pond which Flavian knew held a large gator hole. The holes are dug out by the gators under water and are almost like an underwater cave. Flavian handed me his Marlin .22 caliber, lever-action rifle. He pulled his "gator hook" off the truck, and we waded knee-deep to the far edge of the pond. The gator hook was home-made from a Model A brake rod fashioned into a hook on the end and attached to a pole made from a long piece of peeled cypress. Flavian ran the hook down into the gator hole and started poking around. Pretty soon he felt the gator grab the hook, and he quickly pushed and twisted the pole down the gator's throat.

He began pulling the gator up, fighting the wildly thrashing pole. He said, "Get ready, Worley. When I get his head above water, shoot him!" So, I levered a round and hoped I was up to this action. All of a sudden, this large gator head popped out of the water, right in front of me. Flavian was holding on to the pole as the gator was fighting the hook. I fired and missed a three-foot shot.

Flavian calmly said, "Now take your time, William, and shoot him right between the eyes." Thank God, my next shot was right on the mark, and we had a nice seven-foot hide, which brought $5.00 a foot in those days. This was the beginning of my years of hunting gators for the hide market.

••••••

One lovely spring day in about 1957, Flavian and I were riding on Mickler Road just where the Guana culvert crosses. Flavian said, "Have ya ever shot a gator with a pistol?" I said "No, but I have always wanted to!" At that time, I had a sweet little High Standard .22 LR revolver that I loved to shoot.

So about 10:00 p.m. we launched a little jon boat on the south side of Mickler Road. I was in the bow with my pistol and both of us were wearing our head lights. Flavian was in the stern pushing us along with a cypress pole. The night was still—without a breeze—with the moon shining on the glassy water. It was a beautiful Palm Valley night.

Pretty quick I picked up a pair of those amazing gator eyes, which shine red in the light. Flavian pointed the bow directly toward the gator, and I held the pistol with both hands resting at the bow. The boat captain did a great job of directing the bow and making my shot easier. When the bow approached the gator, I could make out the top of his head. When I fired, the gator stiffened on top of the water just before the bow touched him, I grabbed the closed jaws with both hands and threw this six-footer behind me—almost in the captain's lap!

I immediately heard a loud fight going on in the stern. The gator was only stunned and came to life right at Flavian's feet! When I looked, Flavian was finishing him off with his trusty hatchet. That was too much excitement for one night, so we went home to skin our catch. We never gator hunted with a pistol again!

••••••

From 1960 through 1969, Papa Grover Hughes, my dear father-in-law, and I operated a large livestock farm located on the west side of Jacksonville. We were the second largest hog operation in Florida at that time. The farm was situated on 250 acres of pasture and woods. We usually had over 3,000 head of hogs and a small herd of about 250 Black Angus cattle. We never used a veterinarian in those days, so I handled all of the inoculations and castration procedures.

McGirt's Creek ran through the woods on the western boundary of the property and flowed through the middle of the hog pens. The hogs loved the creek. The creek would rise and overflow its banks whenever we had heavy rains. During these times, the gators would float out of the swamp and into the hog pens. This was perfect for an old Palm Valley boy who grew up hunting gators. Gator hides were still bringing $5.00 a foot back then, which was a lot of money. I killed quite a few gators over those years, but two particular kills stand out in my memory.

#1 - One morning we were cleaning the feed barn and I looked out into the creek on the edge of the woods. There was a seven-foot gator sunning on a log. My Winchester model 94 .30-30 was in the tool shed, so I loaded it with Winchester Silvertip, 175 grain bullets, went around the barn and slipped down to the edge of the creek. Looking back up at the barn, it was like a sporting event with the spectators all lined up looking down at the action. I rested on a little tree, fired at the gator, and watched him roll into the water and sink. Wading out into the chest-deep water, I dove down and began feeling along the bottom until my hand touched a foot, which did not respond when I gave it a little tug. The spectators in the barn cheered when I surfaced with the kill.

#2 – It was one evening about midnight that I killed my largest gator. The creek was very high in the swamp, and I knew the boys would be floating out that night. After grabbing my rifle and headlight, I checked to make sure the battery to my light was in the pouch of my old hunting vest. Then I headed to the hog pens.

At the edge of the creek, I waded in, scanning the water with my light. Standing in water almost waist deep, I began slowly wading among the cypress trees. In less than ten minutes, my light picked up that pair of gator eyes that glow like flames at night. I checked the rifle's sights to make sure I could see the front sight, which I had polished with sand paper. Everything looked good, so I decided to take a few more steps to get a closer shot. I took three steps and stepped right into a hole on the creek bottom. Fortunately, the hole was deep but not very wide. Coming up on the other side of the hole, I was very happy to see that my light was still burning, even though the battery had been submerged. Those glowing eyes were still burning, and the width of space between his eyes told me he was a large fellow. I raised the old Winchester and fired. The gator thrashed a little and then was still. I grabbed him by the tail, dragged him to shore, and backed my truck down to the creek bank. But he was too heavy for me to load by myself.

Then I went up to one of the farm hand's house to wake up Bud Graham. Of course, Bud was already awake because he had heard the shot and knew what was going on. It was all we could do to get the gator up into the bed of my truck. When I skinned him the next day, the hide measured nine feet.

5

The Wild West Comes to Jacksonville

I wish there had been computer records in the 1960's. If there had been, we would be able to pull up a story that means a lot to me. We would see the headline in the local section of the Jacksonville Journal which read, "The Wild West comes to Jacksonville."

During 1960 to 1969, I partnered with my father-in-law, Grover Hughes and his son Clifford, operating the second largest hog-farm in Florida. We were always feeding at least 3,000 head of hogs and a herd of pure-bred Angus cattle during those years. We would go to livestock auctions every week in Lake City and Madison, Florida.

Most weeks we would sell a semi-trailer load of finished #1 hogs (240 pounds) to the Jones-Chambliss packing company in Jacksonville. Here is what happened on that memorable day in the 60's:

The Jones-Chambliss buyer, my good friend, Wilton Collins, and I were just wrapping up the sale of a load of our finished hogs when we heard a commotion outside. We could see the unloading chute from his office, and as we looked, we saw three Brahma steers break through the unloading barrier and run by Wilton's office.

Each one of the steers weighed 1,000+ pounds, so we knew our afternoon work was cut out for us! Wilton reached behind his desk and handed me a single-shot .22 rifle along with a handful of .22 long-rifle bullets. Wilton said, "Worley, you go shoot as many as you can, and I'll run upstairs and get the government inspector so he can come and certify the meat."

So here I was running through a Jacksonville neighborhood in search of three runaway Brahma steers. Luckily, several people had seen the animals running by and gave me directions and encouragement.

With the help of the neighbors, I found the first steer stopped between two row houses that were about seven feet apart. I pulled back the bolt on the rifle and chambered a round. The steer was about fifty feet in front of me and looked like he would charge any second.

When I raised the rifle to sight and fire, I discovered that the gun had NO front sight; I would need to guess where the sight should be when I fired. Just as I was almost pulling the trigger, a little child stuck his head out of a window, right in my line of sight. I yelled for the mother to keep her babies inside, then sighted again and fired, with apparently no damage to the steer.

Then I fired two more times without apparent effect. I could not believe my aim was that bad, even with no front sight. I watched with disbelief and looked closely at the animal. There were three trickles of blood running from three hits to the temple. The Brahma's knees slowly buckled, and he went down. One down, two to go.

When I walked back to the street, I met Wilton and the inspector. While the inspector checked on the dead steer, Wilton said, "Jump in the truck, Worley. I saw one steer over on the railroad tracks." We drove to the railroad crossing and sure enough there stood a steer standing between the rails.

I guess I was getting the hang of shooting with no front sight, because the steer was looking straight at me and gave me a head-on shot. With that kind of shot, I knew I needed to put the bullet between the eyes. Cattle have a "curl of hair" between their eyes. This is the aim point. This time—shooting out of the pickup—I was lucky enough to place the shot exactly in the "curl of hair." The result of the shot was instantaneous. The steer went down stone dead immediately.

We had no news of the third steer until we arrived back at Wilton's office. He got a call from the City of Jacksonville Fire Department, saying they had a report of a steer diving off the St. Johns River bulkhead near Riverside Avenue. I had way too much excitement for that day, so I told Collins I was taking my hog pay check and going back to the farm.

Later that evening I learned the conclusion of this adventure on the TV news. The scene showed Wilton shooting at the third steer from the deck of a city fire boat. The fire boat went to the center of the river and herded the steer back to the Riverside shore.

So ends the story of an exciting day for this ol' country boy!

6

Wild Hog Hunting

Hunting wild hogs with dogs in what is now the Guana Management Area was a favorite thing to do in the 1940's and 50's. We were able to hunt on the property thanks to the friendship between the Mickler family and the land owner at that time, Mr. Jimmy Stockton. We usually hunted on Saturdays when the men's work week was over.

One Saturday morning we all met at the entrance to the property at the end of Neck Road. What an exciting time this was for this eleven-year-old boy. Before we went down the woods road looking for fresh hog sign, Flavian would instruct me and the other young ones on hog hunt safety. The instruction was simple: "If the dogs chase the hog close to you, be sure you have picked out a good tree to climb."

On this beautiful summer day in Palm Valley, we released the dogs on some fresh sign. The dogs quickly found the hog in a large, thick palmetto patch and the fight was on. The sounds from the palmettos were loud, with the dogs barking and growling. We could see the tops of the palmettos thrashing around and then there was a loud yelp from one of the dogs. Flavian and his brother, Merlin, dove into the patch with their guns. Merlin was completely fearless when it came to hand-catching wild hogs in heavy palmetto brush. He would go right in, grab a hind leg and throw the boar, while the animal was distracted by the dogs. I can't remember what caliber their rifles were. I do remember in later years Flavian liked the Ruger .44 magnum semi-automatic. I don't think that particular gun was available in the 1940's.

Anyway, the hog broke out on the other edge of the palmetto patch with the dogs in pursuit. When the Mickler men got to the spot of the initial fight, they found a wounded dog. The dog had a large, deep cut in his chest from the boar's tusks. The boars rubbed pine gum and sand on their upper and lower tusks, then ground them together, which meant they were always very sharp.

Merlin gently gathered the wounded dog in his arms and laid him in the back of his truck. Later that day he sewed the wound closed with needle and thread and the dog survived.

So, there we were on the west edge of the savannah having our lunch of water, saltine crackers, and Vienna sausage, when right across on the east side this very large, black shape emerged. It was the largest wild boar any of us had ever seen. Even at that distance we could see the unbelievable size of his tusks! We already had one badly injured dog and the rest were tired, so the men decided to call it a day.

That was the last time we ever saw that big old boar. Maybe he swam the Tolomato River and died a natural death!

Worley Faver

7

The Sharpshooter and the Stranger

In the late 1970's, I owned and operated another hog and cattle farm on ninety acres located on the west side of Jacksonville near Cecil Field.

Our family and friends would sometimes gather there to celebrate holidays and special events. On these occasions, it was customary for the men to bring their shotguns for a little clay target shooting.

On this occasion, the usual group was there as well as one stranger who came with one of the relatives. After dinner we gathered with our guns, ammo, and a case of clay targets. We all enjoyed a nice afternoon of shooting, breaking lots of targets but missing a few also.

The stranger turned out to be a pretty good shot, with a good string of consecutive hits. The only problem, he **thought** he was a much better shot than he truly was and commenced to be a bore, by bragging on his performance to the point that we were all getting a little tired of hearing him!

My youngest son, Kevin, decided to put the stranger in his place. Kevin walked to his truck and came back with a sweet little .22 single shot rifle that I had bought for him years before. He had one bullet in his hand. He made eye contact with the stranger and loaded the round in his rifle and said, "Dad, would ya please throw one more target for me?" I said, "Buddy, do you want it straight away or from the side?" He said, "Throw it right to left as hard as you can." I loaded the hand thrower and let it go from Kevin's right side. He fired that one round and broke the target in midflight.

Didn't hear much from The Stranger the rest of the day!!

8

Deer Stories

The most famous deer in Palm Valley was a buck named "Ol' Slue-foot." His story is still recounted whenever some of our old hunting group get together over a few adult beverages. We were much younger then, but it's still fun to remember those bygone days.

When he was young, Ol' Slue-foot injured one of his front feet and thereafter walked with a limp. But he could still run like the wind. For many years he proved the most difficult deer to kill that any of us could ever remember.

The usual hunting group gathered on a cool winter day. Flavian and I had ridden down Mickler Road right at daybreak to look for sign. (Mickler Road was just a little dirt road back then.) We saw a big track where a deer had come out of the Guana headed north to Ben Hammock and the Jamb of Sanchez. This area is now an exclusive development called "The Plantation." This is the story of Ol' Slue-foot's last day.

Flavian Mickler, 4th from left, Worley Faver, 3rd from right, Kevin Faver, 2nd from right

The usual hunting group gathered on a cool winter day. Flavian and I had ridden down Mickler Road right at daybreak to look for sign. (Mickler Road was just a little dirt road back then.) We saw a big track where a deer had come out of the Guana headed north to Ben Hammock and the Jamb of Sanchez. This area is now an exclusive development called "The Plantation."

The breeze was coming off the ocean when we turned the dogs loose on Palm Valley Road at the Four Roads, which was on the west side of Ben Hammock. That way the dogs would be searching for scent into the wind. It was not long before the dogs were baying and the chase was on. Flavian had positioned himself on a trail leading through the Jamb of Sanchez, which was on the north side of Mickler Road. He was carrying his old, Enfield rifle .303 caliber that morning.

We could tell by the excitement of the dogs baying that the chase was heating up. At this point they had probably made visual contact with the deer. In a few minutes we heard one shot coming from the direction of the Jamb of Sanchez, so we started heading in that direction and soon came upon Flavian with a huge buck on the ground. He said, "Ya'll are not going to believe this story!"

Flavian's story: "I was standing in the trail, and I could tell the dogs were pushing a deer real hard and were headed directly toward me. Suddenly, out of the heavy brush, this deer burst out almost in my face. I never had a chance to shoulder my rifle, so I fired from the hip."

So, we gathered around the kill and Merlin exclaimed, "My God Flavian, you have killed Ol' Slue-foot!"

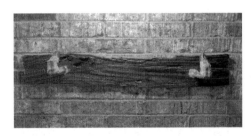

Ol' Slue-foot's front feet reside in the home of one of Flavian's grandsons.

......

On a cool fall morning, our hunting group gathered at the Cow Pen in the Guana. Some of us decided to ride our horses and some brought up the vehicles with the dogs. I was riding my little quarter horse, Fancy, and my friend, Moose, was riding our other horse, Mister, a long-legged old gelding. We found some promising sign east of Jenks Hammock on a trail going through the large clear area of low palmettos. It didn't take the dogs long to flush a buck on the eastern edge of the clearing. The chase headed north toward Jones Hammock.

Moose and I galloped behind the dogs on the old woods road. We came to a turn on the road that looped east around the head of Jones Creek. Moose wanted to go directly through the hammock to Jones creek, but I told him that way was impossible because of the thick underbrush and vines, but he decided to try to go that way anyway. So, we separated.

Fancy and I looped around and came out at the head of Jones Creek and headed west down the open marsh toward Bob Cat Point. I could hear the dogs raising cane and sure enough Fancy and I passed the dogs and saw a nice eight-point buck moving through the marsh grass. I fired my old over/under Stevens 12 gauge and cut the antlers right off the buck's head. The second shot was a little lower and did the job. I went out and retrieved the buck and placed him on Fancy, behind my saddle. I had not seen Moose come out of the Hammock during all this, so I went back around to look for him. He had quite a tale to tell: He said, "Mister and I made it about forty yards into heavy brush, until I rode into a thick web of vines and they pulled me out of the saddle. About that time, I heard two shots and buckshot was clipping branches off above my head." So, Moose was lucky that day when all those #1 buckshot pellets missed him completely.

9

Snakes

The two most important lessons that we learned very young were gun safety and identifying poisonous snakes. In North Florida we have Eastern diamondback rattlesnakes, coral snakes, cottonmouth moccasins, and pygmy rattlesnakes (ground rattlers). Two of my relatives were bitten by ground rattlers, and they carry the scars of those encounters to this day. Barefoot children and ground rattlers are a bad combination.

In those days, anti-venom was unheard of and the only treatment available was "cut and suck." With his scalpel, the doctor would cut "X" shaped incisions all around the fang marks and apply suction to each incision. When we camped out, we carried a snakebite kit, which included a small razor knife, a tourniquet, and several rubber-molded suction cups.

I remember an encounter with snakes in the Guana. This was before the dam was built, so there was no Guana Lake, only a little creek which ran from the ocean at Carter's Run in north Ponte Vedra and flowed south across Mickler Road to join the

Matanzas River. This open space between the woods and the ocean's dunes was beautiful—like a green meadow of marsh grass with a little creek flowing through.

My good friends, Mike, Nath, and I arrived on the east side of the Guana on Friday afternoon and parked our old truck in the woods off A1A. We had all of our groceries and gear and had brought a small inflatable raft to ferry our supplies across the creek. As we walked to the Guana's edge, Nath and I were in the lead and Mike was at the rear. Shortly, we heard Mike holler. I turned and saw a very large diamond back slithering directly towards Mike. This snake will usually either crawl away or coil, but this one was heading straight for Mike who froze and couldn't believe what was happening.

I immediately raised my 12-gauge and fired, killing the snake, which was a very large female. Then we made it to the edge of the creek where we saw a large cottonmouth swimming to the western shore. Once again, I killed my second poisonous snake within ten minutes. The rest of the weekend was wonderful as we slept under the stars on the west side of the Guana, cooking and eating fried squirrel.

••••••

I told my cousin, Steve Hughes, that I would like to have a nice rattlesnake skin to hang in my den. So one day I received this call from Steve and he said, "Come over to my house, I have something for you."

When I arrived at Steve's house, he took me to his backyard where, stretched out on the ground, was the largest diamondback I had ever seen. Steve was hunting that morning in the swamp, which is now the TPC Golf complex, and found this snake sunning outside his gopher hole. I skinned the snake and salted the hide, took it home and mounted it on a cedar plank twelve inches wide and eight feet long. The snake was seven feet, two inches long. My only regret is that I didn't have the skin professionally mounted, because after about five years it began to deteriorate.

Let me close this chapter with an interesting insight into an old Palm Valley superstition: One summer afternoon when I was about ten years old, I shot a cottonmouth and hung him on a nail on one of the live oaks next to The Big House. Granny came out and saw what I had done. She said, "Take that snake down right now, because you never hang a snake on a tree. That will cause the worst thunderstorm you have ever seen."

10

The Fish Camp

When I was about ten years old, I would go with Flavian to the Palm Valley Bridge and visit the Fish Camp. Uncle George Oesterreicher was the owner and was there every day. I always loved Uncle George. He was always smiling and made this little guy always feel welcome.

The sign over his door said, "Palm Valley Package Store." His establishment was the only place in Palm Valley that sold adult beverages. The only other store in the Valley was Hunter's Grocery Store. Uncle George also rented fishing boats. They were made of cypress and probably never exceeded twelve feet in length. The rental fee included a pair of wooden oars. These visits brought back memories of Daddy and me setting out from the Fish Camp on Saturday mornings.

I remember going south down the Tolomato River with Daddy who was an expert boatman and made rowing look easy, which it surely isn't. He would row down the river, and we would stop and fish the mouth of the creeks down to about marker #3.

So fast forward many years and you will find my son, Kevin, and me repeating this ritual. The old wooden boats were still floating, but we were really up-town because we didn't need the wooden oars; we had a 5-horse Johnson outboard motor. We would motor down the Tolomato River without pulling on the oars. Now a 5-horse motor would not push the old boats very fast, but there was an advantage to that. The trip down to marker #15 (our favorite fishing spot), gave us plenty of time for observing and identifying the birds and animals along the way. We saw marsh hens, osprey, eagles, great egrets, great blue herons, raccoons, sea gulls, wild hogs, and alligators. One special day we had a swimming, six-foot rattlesnake try to come aboard our boat. Guess he was tired of swimming against the current.

We would anchor at marker #15 and throw out a dead shrimp with the corks set pretty shallow. There's a shell bed on the side next to #15 with a little cut leading to the marsh behind. The redfish love this spot, and we could usually catch our supper. Kevin, who these days is a well-known charter captain, says that the bass still gather there on the falling tide.

What great days those were! Looking back now, after fifty-plus years, those were days I would so much like to repeat!!

11

Fast Gun

So there I was, living on the Jacksonville Westside, owning and running a large hog/cattle operation with my dear ol' father-in-law, Grover Hughes. I was twenty-four years old with a beautiful wife, Dena, and baby girl named Cindy. I was still in that phase of my life when I "thought" I was bullet-proof and invisible. Ol' Palm Valley boy raised with guns and hunting way before pre-teens.

In those days, we did have electricity, but no air conditioning. We even had a small Sears and Roebuck TV which aired my favorite weekly show, Gun Smoke, with James Arness as Marshal Matt Dillon. After I watched the marshal gun down several bad guys, a thought came into my young mind. "I bet I could learn to fast draw just like my hero."

There was another story circulating back then that really impressed and motivated me. I read about two bad guys robbing a 7-11 store in Texas. The robbers came out the front door of the store with a bag of money and pistols cocked. They saw a man getting out of his car and pointed their pistols and ordered him back into his car. The bad boys did not realize that this gentleman was a Texas Ranger who had the fastest draw on the force. With two guys pointing loaded and cocked pistols in his face, in one lightning move the Ranger moved his coattail aside, drew his weapon and fired twice, centering both robbers in the chest. End of that story.

So, then I went to Tower's Sporting Goods in downtown Jax on Bay Street. Jack, my favorite salesman, showed me a High Standard 9-shot, double-action .22 caliber revolver, blued black with pearl grips; love at first sight. Next stop was my leather guy, who created a fast draw holster and belt, custom made to fit the pistol.

Many hours were spent in front of a full-length mirror practicing the fast-draw move and dry firing. Fast forward several weeks, fast drawing and live firing, I thought I was ready to show someone what I had learned.

Dena and I went down to the creek bank. I set up several beer cans for targets and proceeded to puncture them after my fast draw, which was very fast if I do say so myself. After about six successful fast draws, I guess I really tried to push the envelope, and on the last shot the pistol had not cleared the holster when the weapon fired. The bullet entered the right side of my right knee, severed a fairly important vein, then traveled down the center of my leg and stopped above the ankle. I have always thanked God that the bullet did not hit Dena who was standing right at my side.

During my farm days I had the greatest surgeon friend at Riverside Hospital. He had already patched me up several times from fairly minor farming injuries. His name was Dr. Thad Moseley, a U.S. Army Mash Hospital surgeon during the Korean conflict.

We pulled up to Riverside Hospital and Dena helped me out of the car. Needless to say, the floor board was a little lake of blood. Doctor Thad took a look at a wound he had seen countless times. He sent me over to the hospital and shortly I was in surgery. Next morning, two nurses came in my room and said, "Dr. Moseley wants you up and walking. So, with a nurse on each side, I walked the length of the hall and back. At the end of our little walk—I cannot lie—that ol' knee was doing some hurting, and we had a big old bandage that was soaked. The good doctor came in the next morning and gave me a souvenir – a .22 bullet with a dented red nose.

After all this fun, I decided to hang up the old gun belt and stick with my long guns. I had a cousin, Lavern DeGrove, who really wanted my fast draw outfit, so I traded him for his Model 94 Winchester,

.30-30, which was a sweet rifle. I killed many, many gators with that baby! Now that I'm a retired hunter, my guns reside in a fire-proof vault.

12

The Russian Fisherman

Kevin is my youngest son and quite a well-known charter captain in North Florida. He told me a story of one of his most remembered charters.

One of his radio show sponsors called one January day and asked Kevin if he could fit in a charter for a couple of their best customers. So, one morning at daybreak on a cold morning he met three people at the Vilano ramp: two Russians (one carrying a paper bag) and their interpreter. Kevin should have guessed that this would be a memorable day, but he had no idea!

They ran up the Matanzas River to the Tolomato and began fishing in our old favorite hole just south of Shell Bluff. It was a good morning. Plenty of reds and sheepshead. In late morning, the fisherman reached in their paper bag and pulled out a "handle" of Wild Turkey bourbon, declaring how they loved American whiskey. Then they commenced to imbibe. After an hour or so and several cups of straight Turkey, the fishermen declared they were hot and wanted to have a swim. No telling how cold the old river water was that morning, but it was way too cold for a swim. The fishermen shed their heavy warm clothes and dove off the stern in their Speedo swim suits. After about thirty minutes of an exhilarating swim, they came aboard and continued drinking once again.

The bite was still on and more fish were caught. In mid-afternoon Kevin headed back to the dock with his happy fishermen. He stopped the boat about one hundred yards short of the ramp and the interpreter asked why he was stopping.

Kevin said, "There's no way I can pull up to the Vilano Ramp in front of my fishing friends with two half-naked, drunk Russians! They will have to put their clothes on."

13

Paranda Gator

For years we had an annual outing called "Father & Son Weekend." Probably the most memorable of these fun times was the year we went to a beautiful area we called "The Neck," which is on the west side of the Guana Lake. The old lodge there was called "Paranda," probably from the days when Mr. Jimmy Stockton owned the property.

We slept in tents around the fire, and some of us old guys slept in our sleeping bags on the floor of the lodge. My oldest son, Keith, and his best friend, Neil Hancock, were probably responsible for the unbelievable story I will share here.

There had always been a legend of a famous, very large gator living in the Guana Lake, north of the dam. So, I guess the boys decided they would go out in the middle of the night and find the big gator.

Keith and Neil launched one of the canoes and spent hours looking for the gator. Around 3:00 a.m. they found the old monster gator in about four or five feet of water, lying on the bottom. With my old Winchester, Model 94, .30-30 they took a shot at his head, and the water exploded, almost overturning the twelve-foot canoe! We will continue the story in Keith's own words:

"Then it got real quiet. We found the gator about fifteen minutes later. When he sensed us, he went into a spinning motion, circling from the bottom to the surface. I asked Neil for the rifle and waited for the gator to surface; I shot him again and he stopped moving. It was all we could do to drag him into the canoe. A second canoe held the opposite side of our canoe to keep it from capsizing. The gator was so long that I had to rest his head between my legs, with his tail hanging over the bow of the canoe. I told the guys in the other canoe to go back to camp and make sure the game wardens hadn't arrived as the rifle shot was crazy loud in the middle of the night.

"Neil and I paddled back towards the campsite and stopped about one hundred yards away and waited. Some thirty minutes or so passed and there was no signal from the others. About that time the gator started to come alive in our canoe. Then he started trying to roll over in my lap. I told Neil we were going to take the chance of making it to the landing, but it might be that all three of us were going to end up in the water!

"We paddled for shore as fast as we could and the other boys met us at the dock. They saw me with the gator head between my legs and him turning over in the canoe. They all started yelling.

"When we got close to shore, I jumped out and pulled the canoe on shore. Then we finished off the gator and had a couple of drinks.

"At some point we decided it was a good idea to drag the gator into the cabin and put him behind the bar. What we did not consider was that this same area was where the coffee pot was set up. So about 5:00 a.m., after we had just gone to sleep, we heard a man screaming: 'WTF, Neil, Keith, get your asses in here!' Neil's Dad, Duval, had tripped over the gator in the darkness and almost had a heart attack! We ate gator tail for the next two days."

14

Bourbon

My best friend in high school was Nath. We played football together at Fletcher High School in the mid-1950's and we were both officers in the Senior Class. Nath's mother was a teacher at an elementary school.

We hunted together every hunting season and hosted a poker game in his bedroom every Friday night for our friends at Fletcher. His mother was one of the coolest ladies I have ever known, besides my mother.

During hunting season one year, Nath and I had a good day and bagged several green-winged teal in the Guana creek, before it was dammed and became a lake. We showed up at Nath's home in Atlantic Beach that evening and cleaned our birds. Nath's mother baked them and garnished them according to an old family recipe and they were delicious. Just before she took them out of the oven she said, "This is going to be a special meal for you guys, so I have a recommendation for you. You shouldn't enjoy a meal like this without a little bourbon." So she proceeded to mix Old Fashioned cocktails for two teenaged guys. They were wonderful. I guess that's why at eighty-four years old, my favorite drink is an Old Fashioned! This is NOT the end of this story!

Nath is one of the most intelligent friends I ever had. He graduated with me from Fletcher in 1955 and went directly to Auburn University on a Naval ROTC scholarship. He graduated from Auburn, became a U.S. Marine and went directly to the conflict in Korea. He returned from Korea as a Marine Captain. He then enrolled at the University of Florida and graduated from the law school. He was elected as a judge in Alachua County and served on the bench for many years. He is retired now and we keep in touch. He still owns that house in Atlantic Beach where we used to play poker and had our first drink of hard liquor, thanks to his dear mother.

15

The Aleutian Key

At forty years old, I guess I was a little tired of the corporate world, and after ten years as an officer with a mortgage insurance company in Jacksonville, I left my job.

I told my beautiful wife, Dena, that I needed a little more challenge and excitement in where I went and what I did each day. May God help me, I found exactly what I was looking for. I told one of our friends that I had heard of drilling for oil offshore and was interested in looking into that as a new career. One of our successful and wealthy friends said, "Worley, there is no way you can do that because you are too old, and it will mean learning an entirely new field from the ground up." But I followed my dream anyway.

For nine months I sent out resumes to all of the leading oil exploration companies in America, continually getting negative feedback from my friends. One June day I received a call from a human resources manager of The Keydril Company, an international drilling company in Houston. He said, "Worley, I happened to see your resume on top of the stack on my desk this morning, and I wondered why someone forty years old would want to work in the oil field. I would really like to speak with you. Go to the Delta Airlines counter at the Jacksonville Airport. There's a ticket to Houston waiting for you."

In Houston I met a new friend, Mr. Hugh Roy Robb. We liked each other right away, and I was hired to start working on the maintenance crew on the semi-submersible offshore drilling vessel, Aleutian Key. I reported to

New crew member Worley Faver 2nd from left

Venus, Louisiana, caught the crew helicopter, and reported to my new job which included mopping the deck every morning, chipping rust, sandblasting, and painting.

The rig boss in the oil field is called the tool pusher. The tool pusher for the Aleutian Key was Mr. Wayne Harris from Prentiss, Mississippi. I was the oldest man on the rig crew and Wayne and I became friends right away. My beginning schedule was fourteen days on the rig and fourteen days at home. Lord, how that schedule changed in a very short time.

After chipping rust and painting for six months, I was promoted to maintenance supervisor. Then one  day Wayne called me to his office and asked, "Worley, you've been out here a while. If you had your choice, what job would you like to have on the rig?"

The question really caught me

Aleutian Key Drilling Rig off guard, but I said, "I would love to learn to be a sub-sea engineer!"

So, I was assigned to work under the sub-sea engineer on the rig. I would take a stack of technical manuals home on my fourteen days off and spend my family time studying.

Keydril won a contract to drill the first exploration well in the North Atlantic on Georges Bank, which is located halfway between Cape Cod and Nova Scotia. We started drilling in July and were wearing out diamond studded drill bits on that hard granite ocean floor regularly.

One day Wayne met me on the drill floor and said, "Our sub-sea engineer is

quitting and going to **Roughnecks on the Drill Floor** another company. When do you think you'll be ready to take on that responsibility?" I said, "I'm ready whenever you give me the job!" Wayne said, "I love your confidence!"

After Georges Bank, the rig was towed along the Eastern seaboard headed back to Sabine Pass, Texas. During the tow, we ran into one of those perfect storms. This Florida boy had never seen ocean waves like those. Some of the swells were at least thirty-five to forty feet high. The two ocean-going tugs towing us would go down into the wave trough until you could no longer see them, then they would reappear going up the next wave and the rig would plunge down. We made it safely to Texas and were stacked, awaiting our next drilling contract.

The company received a contract to drill for Petrobras-Brasil. The Houston office instructed me to fly home and stay until the rig arrived at the drilling site 250 miles off the coast of Brasil. I was home for two months, so Dena and I took this opportunity to visit our favorite vacation spot in the Caribbean, Club-Med in Guadeloupe. We returned home after receiving word to fly from Miami to Rio and then by helicopter to São Sebastião, then take another chopper to the rig.

After seven years on the rig, I found myself 250 miles off São Sebastião, Brasil, in the South Atlantic Ocean along with eleven Americans and seventy-five Brasilians.

16

One More Oil Field Story

I would not take anything for those years as sub-sea engineer on a deep-water oil drilling rig; toughest job I ever had, and I had some tough ones.

Running a large cattle/hog operation was how I spent my twenties. Seven days a week beginning at 4:00 a.m. every morning. But that was nothing compared to the oil field! We traveled by airlines, then helicopter to the rig, wherever it was drilling, which could be off the mouth of the Mississippi River in 1,600 feet of water or the first oil well drilled between Cape Cod and Nova Scotia. Toughest of all by far was the oil strike we made 250 miles off the coast of Brasil in 1986. I think this find may have helped the country of Brasil come out of their financial difficulties at that time.

Worley Faver, a tired Sub-Sea Engineer, 1986

My last hitch off-shore was sixty-five days long with work days exceeding twenty-four hours straight.

"One 'day' was forty hours long before I saw my bunk."

Thank God for those great old Cajun girls who would bring my meals to the work area, because I could not leave, due to some challenges we were having with the well.

One night a huge swell came across from the direction of South Africa and hit the rig, "tearing" steel plate like it was paper. This kept our welder busy for a while.

At the end of this marathon hitch, we were in the chopper and something happened that I will never forget! It was a cloudy day, and we were headed to the heliport just outside of Rio. This tired old man looked out the window and saw a beautiful vision. The cloud cover was solid as far as we could see over the city. But I looked and saw CHRIST standing on the clouds with arms spread wide. Of course, if you know Rio, you know this apparition was that magnificent statue overlooking the city from the top of a small mountain known as Christ the Redeemer. The flight home ended those special days in my life!

17

.357

I was fortunate enough to meet and work with many interesting men and women during my years in the oil drilling business. All of our crew came from the Southern states except one named Jimmy. He was a nice guy and did a good job on my crew when I was maintenance supervisor. He left my crew when he was promoted to roughneck on the drill floor. The other guys were from Texas, Mississippi, Louisiana, Alabama, and Georgia. I was the only one from Florida.

One of the quietest and most interesting men was John from Texas. He worked on the drill floor as a roughneck, the most demanding and dangerous job of all. John had those calm, pale blue eyes and was as solid as they come. One day we were taking a break and John told us this story:

"Well guys, I made it home after the last hitch and my wife and I were sitting in the living room having another cup of coffee, when there was a knock at the front door and she got up to see who it was. She opened the door and there was this guy standing there trying to sell something. Apparently, he knew

I was gone a couple of weeks or more each month, and he didn't know I had arrived home the night before.

My wife told him she had no interest in whatever it was he was selling and started to close the door when this guy sticks his foot against the door and started to step into our house. I set my coffee cup down and went across toward him and he immediately stepped back on the porch. I got to the front door, reached over the doorframe and came down with my loaded, Smith and Wesson .357 that resides there. I placed the end of the four-inch barrel under this joker's nose and said, "I hope I never see you again! I don't think I ever will."

I thought this story was timely, because of all the violence and rioting going on in our beautiful USA!

18

Dove Shoot

One of my oldest friends was a wild-man hunter named Robb! We would find dove shoots all over North Florida in the 1960's. I spent many a Saturday with that boy travelling I-10 to Lake City and Live Oak shooting those grey rockets.

Robb was ten years younger than I and was once in my Sunday school class at Collins Road Baptist Church. Those were my days as a Southern Baptist Sunday School teacher, song leader, and deacon.

I never saw Robb back down from anything except gator hunting. He begged me to go one night because he had seen a large gator in a pond in the pasture of his father's dairy. After one night at 1:00 a.m. shining those blood red eyes and standing in water almost to the waist, that boy was DONE with gator hunting.

A really embarrassing thing happened one day when Robb called and said, "I found us a great place to shoot dove this weekend right down Ricker Road from you." I said, "Great, I'll meet you there Saturday at 1:00 p.m."

There we were at 1:30 p.m. at the shoot. I was having an exceptional day shooting my old Stevens over and under 12 gauge. I had killed about six straight birds coming into the field. This gentleman walked up and said, "What's your name?" I told him and said, "I'm here with Robb." And he said, "Who the hell is Robb?"

It was then I knew I was in trouble. He said, "I own this pasture. Get off my land!" Robb thought the whole things was hilarious, but I was not amused to say the least.

The best dove shoots we ever had were at our own pasture at the hog/cattle farm. My brother-in-law, Bubba, and I would invite family and friends every year to shoot in our field. Those are truly some fond memories. Flavian would always be there as would Mr. Carney, our friend who was the best gunsmith I have ever known. He kept all of our guns in perfect working order.

Funny thing happened one year right at twilight. We had a great shoot that day. It was almost twilight, and we didn't want the day to end. Bubba didn't realize he was set up under the birds' favorite tree. When dozens of birds came to the tree for their roost, I will never forget Bubba screaming for help and waving his old John Daly 12-gauge trying to keep the birds off their roost. May God rest your soul, my dear friend!

19

Marsh Hens

The most fun I had shooting birds was every September when the first nor'easter started blowing! The northeast winds always bring the tide up all over the Tolomato river marshes. After the winds blow for a few days, the high tide almost covers the marsh grass. There is a little brown bird living in the marsh by the name, Marsh Hen. No one could cook marsh hens like my sister. They tasted as good as fried chicken, which is as good as it gets. They are really tricky to shoot when they get up and have a thirty mile an hour wind behind them. We spent many a September day shooting lots of shotgun shells at these guys.

One cloudy, windy day in September, Flavian showed up at The Big House in Palm Valley where I was raised and asked Mama, "May I take Worley marsh hen hunting today? The tide is really up." Mama said, "I don't think so Flavian, because he has a bad cold, and I don't think that wading in that cold water will help." Flavian said (God Bless Him) with a straight face, "Ma, I believe that cold water is just what he needs and will really help his cold." I was cured!

So off we go to the marsh to kill our supper. Flavian had a little jon boat with a ten-horse Evinrude kicker to take us down the river. On this day, he had invited an old U.S. Navy pal, Sam, who would be shooting my grandfather's old Model 1897 Winchester 12-gauge pump with a twenty-inch barrel.

We had a great day, killed plenty of birds, and had worked our way down to the creek just west of Black Cook's Hammock. Flavian said, "We've done good today, boys. Let's head for home."

Sam ejected what he thought was ALL of the shells from the old Winchester and thumbed the hammer to lower it when the old worn hammer slipped from his finger and fired a shell left in the chamber.

I was sitting in front of Sam and when the gun fired, I felt the load of shot just miss my midsection. Sam's face was white as a sheet when he asked me if I was all right, which luckily, I was. The real impact of that accident didn't really sink in until I was much older. Anyway, we had many successful marsh hen hunts in later years without any close calls. Thank God, Mama never heard this story!

20

Valley Fishing—1945

When I was eight years old in 1945, things were far different in Palm Valley than what we see today. Life moved at a much slower pace, and there were just a few families living on the only paved road, Palm Valley Road (CR 210). The other roads, such as Canal Boulevard, Roscoe Boulevard, and Mickler Road were all dirt. In fact, Roscoe was just a two-rut woods road.

Daddy drove to Jacksonville to work every weekday morning where for forty-eight years he worked for Robert M. Angas, a civil engineering and land surveying firm.

If it was cold in the winter, we were in the woods with cross-cut saw and axe gathering fire wood. Our only heat in The Big House was two large fire places, and we had to feed those boys. We lived for spring and summer Saturdays when we could head for the canal to wet a line. On Friday nights, Daddy always came home with a pound of dead shrimp, wrapped in newspaper.

Our favorite fishing spots were Henson Ditch and the Big Cypress. Daddy had an old Shakespeare reel, without a level wind, mounted on an old bamboo pole with hand-wrapped eyes. I can remember him cussing when he got the invariable backlash. My fishing gear was a cotton string hand line with a hook and three-ounce sinker. Our sinkers were handmade by pouring melted lead into a mold. Mama and Granny would cook all the drum, bass, sheepshead, and croakers we caught.

We used to see lots of porpoise coming from the St. Johns River and headed to St. Augustine. However, I can never remember seeing a manatee in the canal. Maybe the water was saltier then.

To support this idea, I had a remarkable catch one Saturday. I had thrown out my sinker and bait to the channel and pulled up the slack, and it felt like I had a snag on the bottom. Then pretty soon I was able to gain a little slack. This went on for a while, slowly pulling in whatever was caught on my hook. I had retrieved almost all of my line when a large head broke the surface within fifteen feet from where we stood. The head belonged to a huge sea turtle staring at me with those big eyes. She threw the hook from her mouth with a twist of her head and disappeared.

So, this is how it used to be in the Valley in the old days. I cannot imagine a better life for a young boy or girl, and I am thankful every day for my childhood.

21

Wild Friends

The Palm Valley woods gave my mother and me our favorite childhood pets. Mama was born May 9, 1904 in The Big House.

Her father and brothers kept the family well fed with venison, pork, and squirrels in the wintertime. One winter morning Grandpa and the boys went out with the dogs to try to bag a deer. They didn't kill anything that morning, but one of the dogs caught a fawn. Grandpa brought the little guy home for Granny to take care of while he healed from the dog bite.

Pretty soon the fawn was well and became Granny's companion. The only time Granny became upset with her was when she would slip in the back door through the kitchen and steal bread off the table before everyone sat down to eat. She even became friends with the hunting dogs, and they would play in the yard with the dogs in chase. She grew to be a beautiful, healthy doe and like everyone expected, one cool winter day she slipped back into the woods and was never seen again.

I had two really cool pets from the woods! The first was a three-foot alligator that we caught in a pond one day. I fenced in an area behind the house and even dug him a hole full of water, which he loved. When Granny would cut up chicken for supper, I always slipped him a few pieces. He also enjoyed the little mullet that we caught in the cast net. I learned early on that the boy could not be tamed. He tried to bite me every day until the day I released him back to the pond.

The second pet was easier to care for and really became a friend. His name was Trouble, and Daddy found him one day when a windstorm blew his squirrel nest out of a palm tree. He was a tiny little guy, but was not injured in the fall. I fed him milk from a baby bottle until he was able to eat pecans, which I shelled for him. He grew fast and we became best friends. He slept with me every night and would wake me up at daybreak every morning, racing around under the covers. As he grew larger and older, he became pretty aggressive so I knew it was time to let him go. Even after I let him loose into the woods, he returned sometimes to say hello.

22

Quail, Horses, and Dogs

Imagine looking up a woods trail in thick palmettos, live oaks, and marsh in St. Johns County in the 1890's. This beautiful hammock is bounded by marsh on the east and Pellicer Creek on the south side. The Pellicer is the southern boundary of the county. Coming down the trail on horseback is my grandfather, Alexander Hall Faver, Dr. George Worley (grandpa's best friend), and my great grandfather, Alexander Columbus Faver. They are followed by a horse-drawn wagon of supplies along with a pack of Pointers.

Spending a week in the woods around a campfire with his father, friend, and dogs was one of grandpa's favorite outings every fall.

Great-grandfather had traveled from the historic Faver family home in Greenville, Georgia. Here is a little history of these men's lives:

Alexander Hall Faver was born in Greenville, Georgia, in 1871, moved to St. Augustine as a young man and married my grandmother, Florida Ellen Dykes of Lake Joanna, Florida. He started his own company, Ancient City Wagon Works around 1895.

His business was on Riberia Street in St. Augustine where he had a large blacksmith shop. He built and repaired wagons and carriages. He eventually owned three houses in the area.

Alexander Columbus Faver was born in Greenville, Georgia, in 1848. He rode with the 6th Alabama Calvary during the War of Northern Aggression.

Dr. George Worley was a prominent St. Augustine physician who was lifelong friends with my grandfather. When Daddy was a teenager, he was involved in a serious wagon accident. It appears that his brother was driving the horse and wagon too fast around a street corner. The story said Dr. Worley probably saved my father's life.

The "Worley" name has stayed in our family all these years. It started when my grandpa named Daddy - Samuel Worley Faver.

I know all of us would have liked to have been along on one of those hunts. Grandpa would shoot his old Winchester 1897 12-gauge pump with a twenty-inch barrel, which he had modified.

Thanks to our family, that beautiful piece of property on Pellicer Creek has been preserved. Our family donated the 800 acres to the State of Florida to become the Faver-Dykes State Park to honor my grandparents.

23

H. B. & J. J.

When Flavian and I went into the cattle business in Palm Valley, we named our operation Valley Farms. We went to the cattle auction markets in White House, Lake City, and Live Oak. We were dealing with the same auctions that I used all the years I was in the cattle/hog business in Jacksonville. In a few months we had acquired a nice herd of cows that we judged would make good mamas. They were mostly Hereford/Angus and Brahma/Charolais cross breeds. I had really good results with those breeds at my old farm. All we needed now was an outstanding bull.

Flavian had a pretty famous uncle who raised cattle in Fellsmere, Florida. Uncle Gil Barkoski was a legend in the cattle business in central Florida. It was said back then that at any given time, this region of Florida had more head of cattle than Texas. Florida has always supplied the calf markets with exceptional animals.

Flavian contacted Uncle Gil to see if he could help us in our search for a first-class bull. He told Flavian, "Ya'll bring your truck on down. I have just the young bull you need." So, we made the trek to Fellsmere in my 1975 Chevrolet truck with a cattle cage installed on the bed.

On the way down, Flavian told me a story about Uncle Gil. He said, "One day while Uncle Gil and his hands were loading a shipment of cattle, a rank, old Brahma steer charged him in the loading pen. He ran to climb the fence, but he could see he wasn't fast enough to escape the Brahma's charge. So, he drew the little 9mm automatic pistol he always carried in his waist band and shot the steer six times in the forehead before he reached him.

Uncle Gil also raised some cattle with his brother, Eston, in Palm Valley for a time. We arrived in Fellsmere, ate lunch with Uncle Gil and his wife and then went down to the pen to see our bull. He was a fine young Simmental bull weighing about 800 pounds. When we started pulling out of Uncle Gil's place, he said "Y'all will like this little bull because he is a "horny bastard." So, after that day our bull was known as H. B.

There was one guy back home that never got along with H. B. and that was Flavian's pit bull mix by the name of J. J. Now J. J. was a bad ass who would catch anything Flavian put him on, and he never liked H. B. from day one.

When we were working the cattle every fall, J. J. would remain chained in the truck unless we needed him. Invariably, there would be a cow or two who my quarter horse and I could not cut through the gate. When that happened, Flavian would unchain J. J. and simply point to the cow. J. J. would catch the cow by the nose, and Fancy and I would push her through the gate.

One day during this action, J. J. decided he would like to catch H. B. So, after we got the cow into the pen, J. J. ran over and caught H. B. by the nose. This did not make H. B. very happy, so he just flicked that big old head, and J. J. must have sailed thirty feet into the air, came down, hit the ground and immediately tried to catch H. B. again. We broke up that fight and chained the boy back in the truck.

24

Yellowstone

In 1976 Dena and I decided to take a special vacation with Kevin and Keith in celebration of Independence Day. We boarded our new 1975 Chevrolet and set out. We drove 5,600 miles in seventeen days and enjoyed the best vacation ever! We reserved lodging a day ahead during the trip. The best stop of all was spending a week in Yellowstone National Park where Dena had reserved a cabin in the park.

It was summertime, but the boys were still able to play in the snow in the high country. One morning Dena and I hiked into the mountains. The temperature was probably thirty degrees. As we walked up a slight incline, we noticed that the ground dropped into a little draw just ahead of us. I noticed something strange as we walked up the slope. There was vapor or steam coming from the gully. When we reached the top and looked into the draw, we saw something we have never forgotten. As we looked down into the gully, about thirty huge elk rose to their feet and stared at us. The vapor we saw was from their breathing in the cold air. This was quite a sight for two Southerners.

The next day, Keith, Kevin, and I decided to go fishing in the Yellowstone River. We went to the local outfitter and purchased three sets of fly-fishing gear. Now these old North Florida boys had never held a fly rod in their lives, so this was gonna be a cool day.

After parking, we began walking to a quiet portion of the river. As usual, Keith wandered ahead, off the path and into the deep woods. We suddenly heard a crashing sound from the woods where he had entered. It sounded like a bulldozer going through the brush and trees.

Keith came running out and said, "Ya'll are not gonna believe what just happened!" He had walked right up on a bull moose bedded down in the woods. The moose jumped up and charged away through the brush like a "bulldozer."

So, after that excitement, we made it to a quiet part of the river. We tied some funny looking flies onto our lines and started learning how to cast. We could see cut-throat trout among the pebbles and stones in the crystal-clear water, but they did not want our flies, so like any Southern country boys would do, we improvised. **Fly fishing purists may not want to read any further.....!** We decided the fish needed more than these puny looking little dry flies, so we caught a wide variety of insects and placed them on the hooks of our flies. The trout loved the bugs, so we had a great catch and release afternoon.

That was thirty-four years ago, and we still reminisce about that great vacation when we are having bourbon and cigars.

25

The Rain Crow

For the last story in this book, I want to tell what it was like for a young boy to have a great mentor and teacher like Flavian Mickler.

When Flavian came back from fighting in the Pacific during World War II, I was nine years old. We hunted and fished together for years in Palm Valley. I spent many weekends over the years with my sister, Jackie, and Flavian. He taught me everything I know about hunting and fishing, identifying animals from their footprints, walking in the woods quietly, gator hunting, etc. Best of all though were the stories he told me about days gone by in Palm Valley. I have to tell one story that I still remember like yesterday:

We were sitting out in the yard one lovely spring afternoon, and I heard a bird call that I didn't recognize. I said, "Mike, what was that bird call?" And just then the call came through the thick canopy of the trees again! Flavian says, "That's just an old rain crow; they usually call when rain is on the way."

 It was many years before I actually saw one of these remarkable birds. I heard the call one day, looked up on the tree limb, and there sat a very nice mourning dove; my teacher had played a trick on me. So now that I am old, I still laugh and think of him every time I hear a mourning dove call. May God rest your soul my brother!

The End

If you would like to learn more about early 20th century life in Palm Valley, check out my first book in the *Palm Valley* series, *River of Time*. Both books are available at Amazon.com.

Made in the USA
Columbia, SC
08 September 2021